# The Secrets of Hope the Honey Bee

With Love
Bee Happy
Dr Gerry Bee
x ☺ x

Dr Gerry Brierley

1st Edition March 2019

ISBN: 978-1-9160553-0-8

Illustrations: Sam Foreman. Full composition line drawings: Hope; Eve; Luna; Clarabelle; Nancy; Fanny; Adam; Louis Duke; Quenby; Lilibet; Queenie; Betty. Partial composition line drawings: Pippa; Undine; Prince.

Typesetting: David Siddall, Monmouth, UK
www.davidsiddall.com

Dr Gerry Brierley Ph.D MA Dip.M
www.QueenBeeTalks.Buzz

# Contents

To *Apis Mellifera Mellifera*, the British honey bee,
whose healing venom saved my life, and to my
best friend Bluebell who stayed by my side.

My love to Pru, with a big thank you!

My gratitude is extended to Sam Foreman for
her contribution to the illustrative line drawings.

And to Nancy for showing me the way.

*Dr Gerry Brierley*

*Dr Gerry has excelled in bringing to life the tale of the
honey bee world in this wonderful book.*

Eve Puttergill – Founder of The Bee Effect

www.bee-effect.co.za

# Hope the Honey Bee

As another day dawns on the dewy green lawn, the sun is rising and I feel like flying, before I do, I want to share with you, the secrets of our lives deep inside the beehives. We will tell you our story in all its glory. My name is Hope the Honey Bee and there are many like me. I have thousands of sisters and brothers, we all live in the hive together, along with our golden treasure. Life begins with a new baby girl born in early spring. Our first baby bee girl to be born this year, we named Eve the Egg, and she is tucked up in her bed.

# Baby Girl Bees

# Eve the Egg

Hello! My name is Eve the Egg. I am a little girl egg tucked up in bed. Some say, I am quite an egghead. I will be here for 3 days after Queenie lays. *My secret* is that I am the smallest bee in the hive, yet very alive. Clarabelle the Cleaner Bee cleaned my bed before Queenie the Queen Bee put me here, then she disappeared! Can you see Queenie's lemon footprints as she sprints? Nancy the Nurse Bee is looking after me and feeding me special baby bee Royal Jelly, from the bee deli. Soon, I will change from an egg into a larva and look just like my sister Luna, who is wrapped up like a can of tuna!

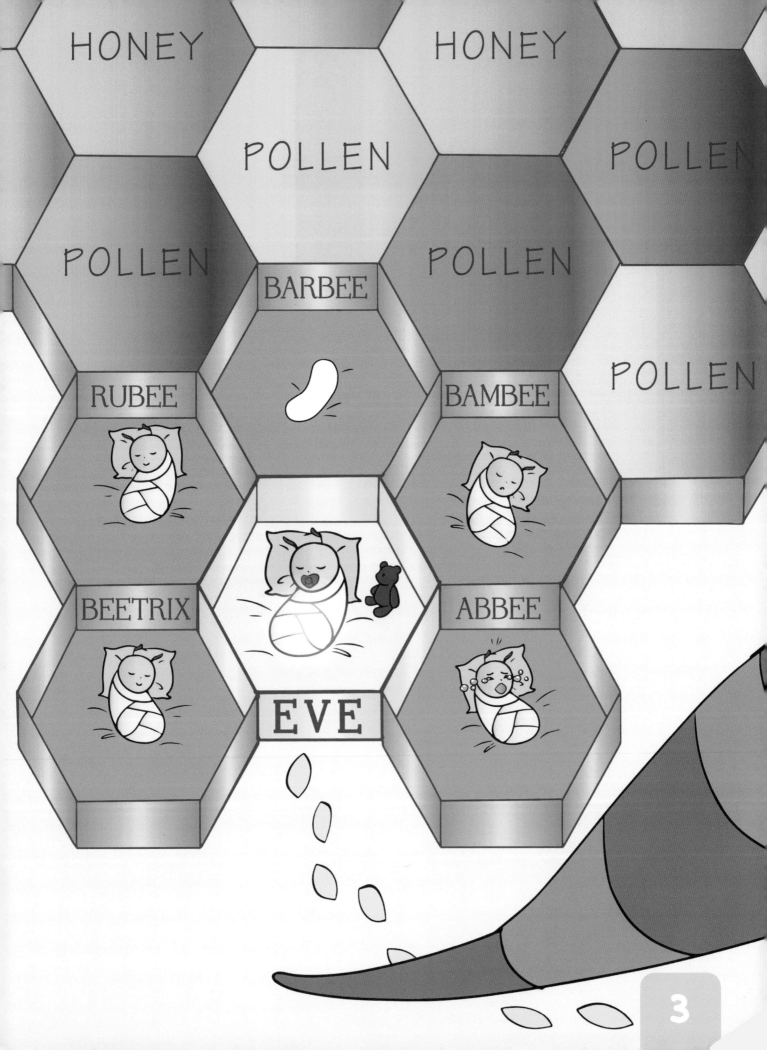

# Luna the Larva

Hello! My name is Luna the Larva. I will be here up to 8 days, after Queenie lays, and will change in many ways. I am white and glow like the moon, in my cocoon. **My secret** is that I have just changed from an egg to a larva, and I will change my skin 5 times, yet I still have lines. I am soft and wobbly, with eyes that are bobbly. I am dreaming of future meadows while I doze, where the bright sunshine glows and hedgerows grow. Nancy is feeding me yummy pollen and honey to fill my tummy. Soon, I will look much cuter, like my sister, Pippa the Pupa.

# Pippa the Pupa

Hello! My name is Pippa the Pupa. I will be here up to 21 days, after Queenie lays, then I will see the sun's rays. I am not so wobbly now and beginning to look like a grown up bee, can you see? **My secret** is that I have grown a long thin tongue, even though I am ever so young, this will give me the power, to get food from deep inside a flower. Bluebell the Beeswax Bee kept me safe by putting a lid on my honeycomb home. Fanny the Fanning bee keeps me warm in the cold and cool when it is too warm, while I transform. Soon I will grow into a big adult bee and break out of my cell, just like Clarabelle.

7

# Worker Bees

# Clarabelle the Cleaner Bee

Hello! My name is Clarabelle the Cleaner Bee, as you can see, and a house worker bee. *My secret* is that I scratched my lid and hatched. Today, I have to clean and make my bed, where I have been eating bee bread. I have been sleeping for 21 days, and now I can see the sun's rays. I am 1 day old, bold and gold. My new wings are fresh and free, and I can fly just like a bee. For the first three days, I must help my sisters clean and prepare the beds, so that Queenie the Queen Bee, can lay more eggs. Next, I fancy, to become a nurse bee just like my auntie Nancy.

# Nancy the Nurse Bee

Hello! My name is Nancy the Nurse Bee as you can see. **My secret** is that from days 4 to 12, I am a house worker bee, and I am studying for a degree. Medicine is my thing, specialising in bee stings. I have long pointy things on top of my head called *antennae*, these help me feel and smell everything, including our offspring and a bee sting. I am very buzzy now working in the hive to make our family thrive. I look after the baby girl bees like Eve, also the baby boy bees like Adam, whom you will meet very soon, he also lives in our bee commune. Next, I will graduate and become an attendance bee just like Atara, who tends the tiara.

# Atara the Attending Bee

Hello! My name is Atara the Attending Bee, as you can see, and a house worker bee. **My secret** is, that between days 7 to 12, I tend to Her Royal Highness Queenie the Queen Bee's every need, whilst she leads, and sows the seeds, of lots of little bees. There are many bees like me, we form a circle around Queenie the Queen Bee, and follow her everywhere she goes, tidying her clothes, before we go off to the meadows. I help spread Queenie's lemon perfume around the hive, so my sisters know she is still alive. Long live the Queen! She is a good old bean. Soon, I will become an undertaker bee just like my sister Undine, which is a whole new routine.

# Undine the Undertaker Bee

Hello! My name is Undine the Undertaker Bee, as you can see, and a house worker bee. **My secret** job between days 3 to 16 is to be the undertaker bee, who cleans up debris. When their time arrives, I will deliver my beloved sisters and brothers to their caretakers high in the sky, to the heavenly hive. We only have short lives of 6 weeks in the summer and up to 6 months in the winter, when we keep warm as a cinder. We huddle in a ball against the cell wall, until spring comes, when we come out and see our chums. Soon, I will grow and become just like my sister, Nadetta the Nectar Collector, which is more fun than being a funeral director.

# Nadetta the Nectar Collector

Hello! My name is Nadetta the Nectar Collector, as you can see, and a house worker bee. **My secret** job between days 12 to 18, is to work in the honey canteen. I collect the nectar from my sister and field forager Honeydew Honey Bee, when she returns from the trees and flowers, between the spring showers. From tansy to pansy, there is plenty for Nancy. Whilst I sit, it is my bee spit, which I mix with the nectar to make this a divine spectre. This is how I make yummy honey, which is good for your tummy. Tomorrow I will grow, and the honey will flow. Yet, I have another job to do, to make dreams come true. Fanning is my next duty, with Fanny the Fanning Bee, who is such a cutie.

# Fanny the Fanning Bee

Hello! My name is Fanny the Fanning Bee, as you can see, and I am a house worker bee. **My secret** job between days 12 to 18, is to be a cooling machine, and a heater, what could be neater. I use my wings to fan, so we can reach our lifespan. I keep my young sisters and brothers at the right temperature, which I ensure, as I take my fanning tour. Too hot is not good, and too cold is not good, we like it just right at 34 degrees centigrade, so no need for first aid. I must keep the honey in the honeycomb cooler than the baby bees in their beds, so they can grow larger than eggs. When I am free from fanning duty, I help my sister, Bluebell the Beeswax Builder Bee, who is making beeswax in 3D, what a bee!

19

# Bluebell the Beeswax Builder Bee

Hello! My name is Bluebell the Beeswax Builder Bee, as you can see, today, I am a house worker bee. **My secret** job between days 12 to 35, in the hive, is to use my magical talent to make beeswax with my body, it's my favourite hobby. My wax is a beautiful golden yellow colour, smooth and shiny like butter. Betty the Beekeeper helps us get started, by giving us some frames with beeswax, which she imparted. I make perfect hexagonal honeycomb shapes, better than any landscapes. I use my mouth and antennae, in such a way, to measure the thickness of the honeycomb, to build our home. Soon I will become like Gerrie the Guard Bee, and give visiting bees the third degree.

# Gerrie the Guard Bee

Hello! My name is Gerrie the Guard Bee, as you can see, and a house worker bee. **My secret** job between days 18 to 21, is to be the guardian of the hive, and to keep my family alive. I sit at the front door while bees come in from the outdoors, most are my family, who I adore. I will let visiting bees into our home if they bring my family gifts of pollen and honey, I don't want their pocket money. Soon, I will grow up to become a field forager like Faerwald. This is when I will leave the hive, go on adventures far and wide, and let the sun be my guide.

# Forager Bees

# Faerwald the Field Forager

Hello! My name is Faerwald the Field Forager bee between days 24 to 42, Woohoo! *My secret* is that I was given this name because I am a great explorer, who travels across borders. I will create a map of this new world outside, before I take off and glide over the hillside. The sun shows me the way during the day. I will find landmarks, which will be my path, to find my way home, back to the honeycomb. I can find honey, pollen, propolis and water using my special eyes and the maps in my head, even at full speed ahead. I fly like an acrobat and wear a pilot's hat. Sometimes, I bump into Polly the Pollinator on my flight, she is such a delight.

# Polly the Pollinator

Hello! My name is Polly the Pollinator bee between days 24 to 42, Woohoo! *My secret* job is to fly around the countryside talking to the flowers, plants and trees, helping to spread news to all their friends and families. In return they give me pollen for calling and talking. I can spread news to millions of flowers, each day, in the same way. I shop in the fields, hedgerows and forests for special pollen food, for our bee brood. I dive into flowers and carry the pollen home in baskets on my back legs, to put in our beds. It is now early summertime, and I bumped into Honeydew Honey Bee before bedtime.

# Honeydew Honey Bee

Hello! My name is Honeydew Honey Bee between days 24 to 42, Woohoo! *My secret* job is to go shopping for honey food for my family in the woods, meadows, hedgerows, forests and coppice, I see more flowers than a florist! I visit up to *2 thousand* plants and trees every day in the summer, while I hummer, not bad for a little newcomer. Sometimes, I collect extra honey food for our friend, Betty the Beekeeper, who is our cheerleader. Bluebell the Beeswax Builder Bee makes lids to keep our honey forever fresh, for our little crèche. When I returned home, Pru the Propolis Bee was repairing our hive, she deserves a high five!

# Prue the Propolis Bee

Hello! My name is Prue the Propolis Bee between days 24 to 42, Woohoo! **My secret** job is to visit the trees and plants, and they give me gifts of sticky glue called propolis to take back to the hive, which helps us stay alive. I chew this propolis in my mouth to give it special healing powers, from many flowers. My sisters also use it to clean the comb and fill any gaps and cracks, in the beeswax, to keep us warm, in a storm. When I returned home to mend the comb, Skye was doing a special dance, and she has put the little bees in a trance.

# Skye the Scout Bee

Hello! My name is Skye the Scout Bee between days 24 to 42, Woohoo! *My secret* job is to look for new homes and meadows, and to find out where the best food grows. I fly into the sky and dance with ease on the breeze, looking to view pastures new. I help Queenie the Queen Bee look for a new home, when ours becomes too small, we will curl up in a ball and I will lead the forager swarm, but not in a rainstorm. When I return home I do a special dance on the comb for my sisters called the *waggle dance*. I wiggle and waggle my bottom and buzz my wings to show them the way to the special meadows, where our food grows and water flows. Can you do the waggle dance? *You put your bottom in the air, like you just don't care, turn around in a circle, and buzz your wings until they start to ring*. Oh look! It's Roberta the Robber, who has got herself in a bit of a bother.

# Roberta the Robber Bee

Hello! My name is Roberta the Robber Bee between days 24 to 42, Woohoo! **My secret** job in autumn, when the leaves begin falling, is to borrow honey from other honey bee hives. I have to get past the guard bee, which is not easy. I bring the honey home to share with my sisters and brothers to help our lives, so that we may thrive. I only do this when we are hungry in late summer and autumn to help us stock up our honey pantry, especially for Nancy. This is a very buzzy and stressful time to be a honey bee, because we need to prepare for the winter, you see.

# Baby Boy Bees and the King Drone Bee

# Adam the Egg

Hello! My name is Adam the Egg. I am a little boy egg tucked up in bed. I will be here for 3 days after Queenie lays. I am larger than Eve, which is not hard to believe. **My secret** is that, being a boy bee, I will not grow a stingy tail like Eve. Clarabelle the Cleaner Bee cleaned my bed before Queenie the Queen Bee put me here, then she disappeared! Can you see Queenie and her lemon footprints as she sprints? Nancy the Nurse Bee is looking after me and feeding me special baby bee Royal Jelly, from the bee deli. Soon I will change from an egg into a larva, and then I will look just like my brother, Louis, who is all white and dewy.

# Louis the Larva

Hello! My name is Louis the Larva. **My secret** is that I am a boy larva and I will be here up to 10 days, after Queenie lays, and will change in many ways. I look similar to my sister Luna, though I need to grow larger than Luna, but I won't hatch any sooner. I am also soft and wobbly, with large eyes that are bobbly. Nancy the Nurse Bee has been feeding me lots of yummy pollen and honey to fill my tummy. I am dreaming of playing in the sky when I become big and strong, like Duke the King Drone. First, I must change my skin and begin, to grow into a pupa, like my brother Prince the Pupa.

# Prince the Pupa

Hello! My name is Prince the Pupa. **My secret** is that I have a home shaped like a dome and I will be here up to 24 days, after Queenie lays, then I will see the sun's rays. My home is larger than Pippa's, yet I am still a nipper. I am not so wobbly now and beginning to look like a grown up bee, can you see? Bluebell gives me a special lid to keep my head safe. Fanny the Fanning Bee will keep me warm in the cold and cool in the heat, by fanning me with her wings, which makes me feel like a king. I am beginning to look a lot like my brother Duke the King Drone, almost a clone, but without a throne.

# Duke the King Drone Bee

Hello! My name is Duke the King Drone Bee. **My secret** is that, on day 24, I open my door, so no more time to snore. I have just lifted my dome, to break free from the honeycomb, which has been my home. I am the bees knees, and hang out in honey pantries. Hurrah what a bee, I hear you shout with glee! With huge eyes to find my prize, I am ready to zing, and become a king. I don't work hard like my sisters do, I just look fabulous in blue, and fly with the drone aircrew, keeping princesses in my view. In my dreams, princesses become queens, so I can't wear my old jeans. In a suit and spats, I am quite a catch. I like honey for a tipple, sometimes it's a triple!

# The Princess and the Queens

# Quenby the Queen Egg

Hello! My name is Quenby the Queen Egg, I will be here up to 3 days after Queenie lays. **My secret** is that I am a very special little egg as someday, if I am lucky, I will be a queen. My name means 'little queen'. I am chosen by my sisters, not by misters, but first, I must become a larva and a queen cell before I become a princess, and wear a fancy dress. I live in a round bed shaped like a cup called a **queen cup**, which will soon fill up. Nancy feeds me Royal Jelly, from the bee deli, which she makes in her head, and she puts it in my bed. Next I will grow and look like Lilibet the Queen Larva, and become a lot larger.

# Lilibet the Queen Larva

Hello! My name is Lilibet the Queen Larva, I will be here up to 8 days after Queenie lays. **My secret** is that I am different from Luna the Larva, because I bathe in a pool Royal Jelly, and eat it to fill my belly. This means I will live up to 5 years, which deserves 3 cheers. Some say long live the queen, but I am not yet 16. Sometimes, I give some Royal Jelly to my friend, Betty the Beekeeper, so she can be healthy and strong just like me, the queen bee. Soon, I will become a pupa just like Quenna the Queen Cell, and grow very well, in my queen hotel.

# Quenna the Queen Cell

Hello! My name is Quenna the Queen Cell, I will be here up to 16 days after Queenie lays. **My secret** is that I am called a *swarm cell*, which is like a shell, a sort of queen hotel made by Bluebell. Bluebell the Beeswax Bee will build me a sealed lid on day 8, so our queen will lose weight, in readiness for her escape. My home looks like a large peanut and I quack like a duck, and hang upside down like a bat, not like a beautiful queen bee at all! **Quack quack! Quack quack!** When I hatch, I will look just like Prospera and wear a tiara, I am a princess in waiting, until I start dating.

# Prospera the Princess Bee

Hello! My name is Prospera the Princess Bee. **My secret** is that it is day 16, and, I am nearly a Queen. I have hatched into a beautiful princess bee, with a long body and large wings, I will fly with kings who will give me rings. I make a *piping* noise to warn other princess bees that I am here, as they have much to fear. We might fight, or escape into the daylight, with a small band of followers, who will be our personal warriors. I am ready to steal the crown from Queenie the Queen Bee, who is buzzy taking afternoon tea! **Pip pip! Toot toot!** Here I come… **Pip pip! Toot toot!** I am tooting and planning on doing some looting. The crown is my jewel, and when Queenie has run out of fuel, I will be her renewal.

# Queenie the Queen Bee

Hello! My name is Queenie the Queen Bee, can you see me? I have a beehive hairdo, to give you a clue. **My secret** is, that I am head of the honey bee family and the mummy of all the bees. Queens can have long careers, and live for 5 years, now that deserves 3 cheers! I have flown with many kings and we meet in the sky to dance and sing. I can lay up to *2 thousand eggs*, just like Adam and Eve every day. My faithful followers bring me food, and tend my brood. My shoes are made from lemons, they are my secret weapons of perfume, so I rule in every room, during the baby boom. Prospera the Princess Bee is on the prowl to steal my crown, and be the new top girl in town. I must become lean and let Prospera become queen. Many forager bees like Faerwald will follow my tail, and Skye the Scout Bee will show us the trail. We travel huddled together in a swarm. Don't be alarmed, we are ever so calm. Sometimes I might rest in your garden. I do beg your pardon. *Bye bye until we meet again.*

# Betty the Beekeeper

Hello! My name is Betty the Beekeeper, the honey bee seeker. One day, when I looked through the window and saw Hope the Honey Bee, I knew she was right for me. So, I gave her a hive, and now Hope and her family thrive.

I look after the honey bees and they look after me. Don't worry, I have spoken with Queenie, and I will give Queenie a new home of comb. I caught her just in time before Prospera committed her crime!

Hope and her sisters provide, far and wide, for the countryside. They help all humans have enough food to eat, which is more than a treat and very neat. Hope whispered in my ear that she is a healing bee, so, you see, *my secret* is that when I got sick from being bitten by a tick, I was so frail, Hope gave me some drops of medicine from her stingy tail, and I am still here to tell you the tale. Hope made me well again and I have no pain, she will be my friend to the end of time, for treating my Lyme. Hope made all my dreams come true, and I wish the same for you. May this golden treasure, be with you, now and forever.

# The Poem of Hope

Eve the egg tucked up snug in bed
Luna glowing like the moon
Pippa to hatch very soon

Clarabelle makes the beds and spreads her wings
Nancy dances, sings and checks on her siblings
Atara gets food from the parlour and tends the tiara
Look! It's Nadetta, the nectar collector
Fanny fans the little bees to tend to their needs
Bluebell the beeswax bee has a magical talent
All are so gallant

Gerrie guards the gate
Whilst Polly pollinates
So much work to be done
Oh look, Faerwald has gone! Into the field, so much to yield
Honeydew shops for honey
It's free, so no need for money
Prue the Propolis Bee, with glue for you and me
Skye is on the scout, can you see her out and about?
Roberta the Robber can get into lots of bother
Undine is here to show you that death is a part of life,
so have no fear
The little bees are so very dear

Adam the Egg tucked up snug in bed
Louis the Larva will become a father
Prince the Pupa has a dome in the comb
Look! Here comes Duke the drone

Quenby the Egg tucked up snug in bed
Lilibet bathes in Royal Jelly to fill her growing belly
Quenna quacks like a duck and will need much luck
Prospera the piping princess wants to make the hive her nest
To steal Queenie's crown, made Queenie frown
and she nearly left town!
Duke dances on the breeze embracing princesses
with elegance and ease

High in the sky Duke the Drone king arrives
Now a new Queenie returns to the hive,
to create new bee lives
Since Prospera has flown, the seed is now sown
And into a new Queen Prospera has grown
With a new, home grown, crown of her own
Off to a new hive to create many more bee lives

It was true indeed, that Betty met Hope, in her time of need
Betty prayed one day that a solution would come her way
This set off a passion that Betty never thought would happen
Betty the Beekeeper became brighter and now she is a writer
She was empty as a shell and now she is well
From the bees and Hope, a future she sees
Hope can reveal that her family can heal
Hope gave Betty life and now she can write
The truth, you see, is that Betty is me, Dr Gerry Bee
With help from humans, Hope and her family can thrive
If we all work together to keep the hive alive

# About the Author

After a near fatal encounter with blood sucking ticks many years ago in the Surrey Hills, 'Hope' was all I had left. Before this encounter, my life had been exceptional. I lived it full and free. I had been a multi award winning minor British female inventor, innovator and marketer, a Freeman and Liveryman of the City of London, slowly building my reputation. I had been the first female to gain a pilot's licence on fixed wing microlights at my local flying club, and second female to gain a rating on the Seamax flying boat in Europe. Fun times with TV appearances on shows such as BBC Eggheads and Beat the Boss.

During 2006/7 I had found ticks attached to my body while walking in the Surrey Hills, not long after, around 2007/8, I had become frequently unwell with bouts of reoccurring infections, which no antibiotic would heal. After repeated misdiagnosis, in 2011 I commenced a PhD, yet within a matter of months I had become bedridden with pleurisy, pneumonia, malaria like symptoms and raging fevers. Days turned into weeks, weeks turned into months and months into years. Beginning to suffer brain damage I lost my memory and suffered speech and partial facial paralysis. Unable to remember my work or my name, I was admitted to a private hospital where I was diagnosed with two strains of Lyme disease; Mycoplasma Pneumonia; Babesia; Bbartonella and Ehrlichia. Hooked up to antibiotics by IV line, and then with 3 years of further antibiotics and other treatments, it took its toll, it was too little too late. Improved, but still desperately unwell, I found out about how honey bee venom had 'cured' Lyme disease. I had lost most of my hope and with nothing more to lose other than my mortal soul. In May 2015 I took my first honey bee sting and many stings followed. After 3 months I had recommenced my PhD and had become a beekeeper, on a steep learning curve into the mystic art and science of beekeeping. Miraculously, two years later in July 2017 I graduated with my Doctorate. In 2017 I was initiated as a Druid, which helps me understand our relationship with our ancestors, philosophy and the relation to our earth and creatures great and small. I joined a rowing club and learnt to scull, which helped with my balance. I now scull frequently and will start competing in 2019. In 2018 after 3 years of using bee venom and applying over 4500 stings to my body, I was clear of Lyme but the residual damage lingers. A scientific paper was published in 2017 showing how bee venom was more effective at killing Lyme Disease than antibiotics, how very 'lucky'! In 2018 I began speaking on the subject of 'Medicinal Apitherapy', which is the therapeutic uses of honey bee products, and now speak widely to bee associations and other organisations in the UK on the subject and I tell my story of how bee venom saved my life.

'Hope' was born out of great pain and a passion to get myself well again. I wrote 'Hope' originally for fun and escapism to transport myself to the past many years ago, when, as a child times, thoughts and things seemed unadulterated, innocent, pure and happy.

Finally, out of the eye of the storm I have sought solace in writing fun innocent educational stories to inspire children and the adults who read them to their children and grandchildren. I still marvel at the true wonderment of the honey bee, with a deep sense of gratitude for their healing qualities. I learn more every day about their incredible gifts. My 'Hope' is to transfer the treasures in my heart and mind, to create a fun learning experience for others in the form of my story writing, and to relay the deep meanings and magic within our magnificent eco system, through my flagship book, The Secrets of Hope the Honey Bee.

Dr Gerry Brierley,
March 2019

Printed in Poland
by Amazon Fulfillment
Poland Sp. z o.o., Wrocław

49340246R00040